THE MAGIC COLOR WHEEL

A color wheel, also known as a color circle, is a traditional concept in art and is a visual representation of colors and their relationships on the color spectrum. Color wheels show us how colors are related and are handy to refer to when making color decisions. You can break colors down into several categories based on their positions on a wheel. See the next page for how this works!

COLOR TERMINOLOGY

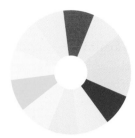

Primary Colors
Red, yellow, and blue.
These are colors at their basic essence; you cannot create primary colors by mixing other colors.

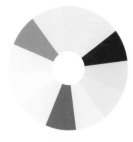

Secondary Colors
Green, orange, and purple.
These are colors achieved by mixing two primary colors. You can also create tertiary colors by mixing a primary color with a secondary color.

GET TO KNOW COLOR

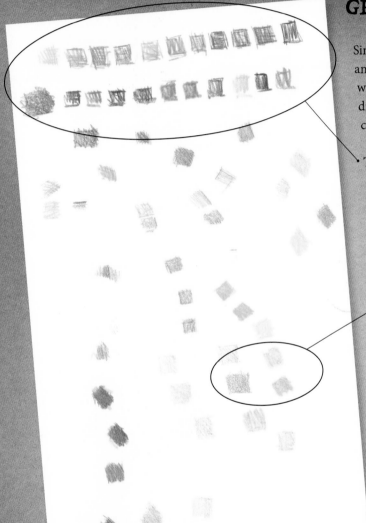

Since the time I could hold a pencil, I have loved drawing and all of the qualities and emotion that lines can give. That's why I have so much fun inking Eric's characters. While I didn't really play with color until I was in college, I now consider myself a complete color junkie!

The fairy (page 3) and the dwarf (page 4) that I colored for this tutorial were both done with two partial boxes of 12 colored pencils. The first thing I did was draw color samples across the top of my practice sheet to see what colors I really had. The colors that you see when you look at your pencil will be somewhat different when applied to your paper. That's why this is an important step!

When I see a color in my head that I want on my coloring page, I test colors on my practice page until I know I have the color I'm imagining.

TIP! To create a color you want that you can't get straight from the box, work in layers of color by using very light pressure. Check out the colors I layered on one area of the dwarf's beard to achieve a specific look. I used blue, then brown, then red, then yellow. It takes a bit of extra time to color this way, but it's worth it! I like the richness of color that I can achieve and the pride of knowing that I created something more than what was in the box.

This tutorial was developed by my wife, Tricia Buck Messinger. Tricia's need to work with her hands led her to pastels, and she's never left. Tricia's soft touch and in-depth knowledge of color has made her a sought-after resource for other artists. She lives quietly in the Texas Hill Country with me, her horses Bella and Mookie, and our full house of cats and dogs.

Complementary Colors
These are colors located opposite each other on a color wheel. They are different enough to provide a lot of good contrast if you want an image to pop.

Analogous Colors
These are colors located close together on a color wheel. They can be warm or cool, or a mix of both. Together they appear harmonious, typically for a calmer effect.

I wanted this fairy's hair to have highlights, so I started with a light layer of red and laid orange and yellow lightly over that. For the areas around her face, I pressed down more firmly with the pencil to give the color a more saturated look.

To give the wings more of a three-dimensional look, I started with a darker color near the inner edges and faded to a lighter color on the far edges.

FAIRY FIRE
THE FIRE QUEEN

Complementary colors (see above) create major visual impact! So I colored this fairy's wrap green to contrast her red hair.

To mimic what our eyes see in the world, I added a bit of blue to the wrap in shadow (around the fairy's back) and yellow to the wrap in light (over the fairy's arm).

To give the filigree on the dress more dimension, I added an analogous color, orange, around the edges of the yellow. I pressed firmly on the paper to make the colors darker and a little more vivid.

HOW DO I MAKE THAT COLOR?

Don't be intimidated by this image! I'll show you how I achieved the different colors and effects. It's easier than you think!

Try building your darks with colors other than black. Using only black for a dark tends to create a dead color. This is also known as the dreaded "Black Hole Effect." By layering your darkest colors, you can achieve a strong dark that is both lively and pleasing to the eye.

You can also build lightly stroked layers toward the light. Here I started with purple in the shadows and built other colors on top to show what is being hit by the light.

I love the challenge of coloring beards! For this beard, I used four layers of color (see page 2).

To create the shadow on this dwarf's skin, I added a very light layer of blue. Remember, objects in shadow tend to have the blue family of colors to them. Blue, purple, or green can work.

When you have busy areas with a lot going on, choose one area that you want to emphasize over the others. Here, I worked to keep my colors softer and more muted, except for what appears on the breastplate. I used stronger complementary colors for this part to help it come forward and stand out.

When you want to color something that's metal, get playful! It doesn't always have to be plain old gray—incorporate some color. Here, since my metal is mainly blue, I made the shadow mostly purple.

DIGITAL COLORINGS

Though I do plenty of coloring by hand (as you'll see in the following pages), I spend much of my time working digitally. Here are some examples of works I have done digitally, some of which provided inspiration for the black and white art for this book.

BENNU IS THE MOST ANCIENT PHOENIX IN EXISTENCE.
IT IS FROM THE ASHES OF HIS EGGS THAT ALL OTHER
PHOENIXES HAVE ARISEN.

Phoenix, page 47.
Colored pencils. Color by Lynette Parmenter.

BELRAK IS A DWARVEN WOODLAND WARRIOR. ALTHOUGH MANY OF THE WOODLAND DWARVES ARE KNOWN FOR THEIR JOLLY NATURE AND SENSE OF HUMOR, BELRAK DID NOT INHERIT THESE TRAITS. WHATEVER YOU DO, DON'T CROSS HIM!

Dwarf Warrior, page 35.
Watercolors (Koi by Sakura). Color by Eric Messinger.

WHAT ARE WE TO DO WITH JOY THE GOBLIN SPRITE? ALTHOUGH SHE LOOKS LIKE HER GOBLIN RELATIVES, HER TEMPERAMENT IS MUCH LIGHTER AND HAPPIER. IT IS BECAUSE OF HER HAPPINESS THAT JOY HAS BEEN ACCEPTED BY THE SUMMER HOUSE OF THE FAE AND ACTS AS AN ADVISOR TO THE SUMMER QUEEN ON GOBLIN MATTERS.

Joy the Goblin Sprite, page 45.
Watercolors (Koi by Sakura). Color by Eric Messinger.

LILLITH IS A WATER DRAGON. WATER DRAGONS ARE SHY AND RECLUSIVE BY NATURE. THEY TEND TO MAKE THEIR HOMES NEAR VOLCANIC ISLANDS IN THE REMOTEST PARTS OF THE OCEAN, WHERE THEY CAN ENJOY THEIR SOLITUDE.

Water Dragon, page 41.
Markers (Spectrum Noir), colored pencils (Prismacolor). Color by Lisa Caryl.

FINN (ACCOMPANIED BY HER JACKALOPE NAMED HARE) IS PART OF THE PIXIE ROYAL GUARD. IT IS HER JOB TO DEFEND THE FOOD STORES AND THE PIXIE LANDS. WHILE SHE MAY BE SMALL, NEVER UNDERESTIMATE THE FIERCENESS OF THE PIXIES!

Finn the Jackalope Rider, page 57.
Markers (Copic, Winsor & Newton), colored pencils (Prismacolor). Color by Lisa Caryl.

RED CLAW THE GRIFFIN IS ANOTHER RECLUSIVE CREATURE. HE MAKES HIS HOME IN THE HIGHEST TREES IN THE DEEPEST PARTS OF THE FOREST. HE IS FRIENDS WITH ALL MANNER OF FAIRY FOLK, AND ONLY THEY KNOW HOW TO FIND HIM.

Griffin Bow, page 21.
Markers (Spectrum Noir), colored pencils (Prismacolor), soft pastels. Color by Lisa Caryl.

ATTOR IS ONE OF THE OLDEST MEMBERS OF THE ROCK DRAGON
CLAN. AS SUCH, HE SHUNS OUTSIDERS. ALTHOUGH LONG-LIVED
AND WISE, HE IS ALSO EXTREMELY TEMPERAMENTAL. APPROACH
HIM AT YOUR OWN RISK!

Ledge Dragon, page 61.
Watercolors (Koi by Sakura). Color by Eric Messinger.

DRAGOON IS A MEMBER OF THE ROCK DRAGON CLAN. WHILE MANY OF ITS MEMBERS ARE KNOWN FOR BEING RECLUSIVE AND TEMPERAMENTAL, DRAGOON IS MORE SOCIAL AND ACTS AS A LIAISON BETWEEN HIS CLAN AND THE OTHER SPECIES IN HIS WORLD.

Dragoon, page 33.
Colored pencils (Prismacolor), acrylics (Liquitex). Color by Ralph Johnston.

SNAAG IS A WAR ORC WHO LIVES FOR BATTLE. HE HAS NO SURNAME OR STRONGHOLD AND MAKES HIS LIVING AS A MERCENARY, PLEDGING HIS ALLEGIANCE TO WHOEVER HOLDS THE MOST GOLD.

War Orc, page 65.
Watercolors (Koi by Sakura). Color by Eric Messinger.

AURELLIA IS THE YOUNGEST PRINCESS IN THE SUMMER FAIRY COURT.
HER SPECIALTIES ARE WORKING WITH AND NURTURING THE FLOWERS
AND SMALLER PLANTS WITHIN THE REALM.

Aurellia, page 37.
Colored pencils (Prismacolor). Color by Kelly Nagorka.

PEGASUS HAS AN IMPORTANT ROLE IN HIS WORLD. HE IS RECLUSIVE AND PREFERS TO WANDER THE MOUNTAINS ABOVE THE REALM OF THE WOODLAND ELVES, WHOSE MUSICIANS ALONE HAVE THE ABILITY TO CALL HIM. WHEN THE NEED IS GREAT, HE WILL ACT AS A MESSENGER. BECAUSE OF THIS, HE HAS HELPED AVERT MANY WARS.

Pegasus, page 39.
Markers (Prismacolor), colored pencils (Prismacolor), gel pens (Sakura). Color by Annie Jump.

LIFE IS EITHER A DARING
ADVENTURE OR NOTHING.

—Helen Keller

Acacius the One-Horned Giant

THE CAVE YOU FEAR TO ENTER HOLDS
THE TREASURE YOU SEEK.

—Joseph Campbell

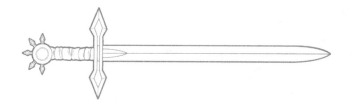

FILL YOUR LIFE WITH ADVENTURES,
NOT THINGS. HAVE STORIES TO TELL,
NOT STUFF TO SHOW.

—Unknown

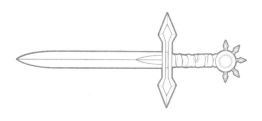

IT DOES NOT DO TO LEAVE A LIVE
DRAGON OUT OF YOUR CALCULATIONS,
IF YOU LIVE NEAR TO HIM.

—J.R.R. Tolkien, *The Hobbit*

Avila the Mystic Dragon

ALWAYS REMEMBER, IT'S SIMPLY NOT
AN ADVENTURE WORTH TELLING IF
THERE AREN'T ANY DRAGONS.

—Sarah Ban Breathnach

Viking Giant with Hydra Dragon

KEEN ARE THE EYES OF THE ELVES.

—J.R.R. Tolkien, *The Two Towers*

Babak the Desert Elf

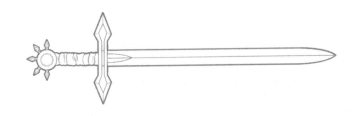

SARAH: OW! IT BIT ME!

HOGGLE: WHAT'D YOU EXPECT FAIRIES TO DO?

SARAH: I THOUGHT THEY DID NICE THINGS,
LIKE... LIKE GRANTING WISHES.

HOGGLE: SHOWS WHAT YOU KNOW, DON'T IT?

—*Labyrinth*

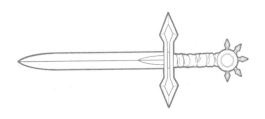

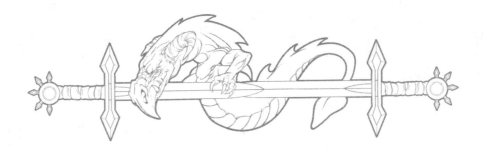

WHERE'S THE GLORY IN REPEATING
WHAT OTHERS HAVE DONE?

— Rick Riordan, *The Lightning Thief*

_____
_____
_____
_____
_____
_____
_____
_____

Chimera

© Eric Messinger • *From Fantasy Adventure Coloring Book* • © Design Originals, www.D-Originals.com

NEVER LAUGH AT LIVE DRAGONS!

—J.R.R. Tolkien, *The Hobbit*

_____
_____
_____
_____
_____
_____
_____
_____

Dragoon

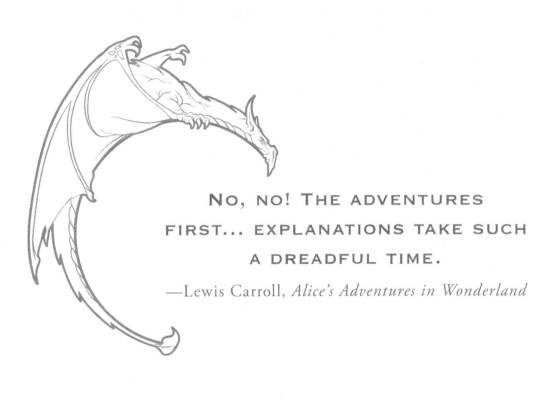

NO, NO! THE ADVENTURES
FIRST... EXPLANATIONS TAKE SUCH
A DREADFUL TIME.

—Lewis Carroll, *Alice's Adventures in Wonderland*

Dwarf Warrior

© Eric Messinger • *From Fantasy Adventure Coloring Book* • © Design Originals, www.D-Originals.com

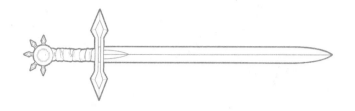

NEITHER COUNTRY PROVERB NOR
KING'S COMMAND COULD KEEP ME
FROM THE WOODS, TODAY.

—*Legend*

Aurellia

© Eric Messinger • *From Fantasy Adventure Coloring Book* • © Design Originals, www.D-Originals.com

THE ONLY QUESTION IN LIFE IS WHETHER OR
NOT YOU ARE GOING TO ANSWER A HEARTY
"YES!" TO YOUR ADVENTURE.

—Joseph Campbell

Pegasus

THE BRAVE MEN DIDN'T KILL DRAGONS.
THE BRAVE MEN RODE THEM.

—Game of Thrones

_____

_____

_____

_____

_____

_____

_____

_____

_____

Water Dragon

© Eric Messinger • *From Fantasy Adventure Coloring Book* • © Design Originals, www.D-Originals.com

WIZARD'S THIRD RULE:
PASSION RULES REASON, FOR BETTER
OR FOR WORSE.

—Terry Goodkind, *Blood of the Fold*

Fairy Fire

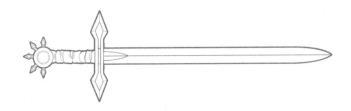

NEVER MESS WITH GOBLINS.

—J. K. Rowling, *Harry Potter and the Sorcerer's Stone*

Joy the Goblin Sprite

© Eric Messinger • *From Fantasy Adventure Coloring Book* • © Design Originals, www.D-Originals.com

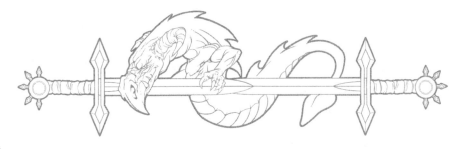

PHOENIXES BURST INTO FLAME WHEN
IT IS TIME FOR THEM TO DIE AND ARE
REBORN FROM THE ASHES.

—J. K. Rowling, *Harry Potter and the Chamber of Secrets*

Phoenix

IT IS ONE THING TO READ ABOUT
DRAGONS AND ANOTHER TO MEET THEM.

—Ursula K. Le Guin, *A Wizard of Earthsea*

Dagr the Dragon

THESE THINGS LIVE ON DEATH
AND FEED ON ASH.

—*Reign of Fire*

_____

_____

_____

_____

_____

_____

_____

_____

Dragon Hunter

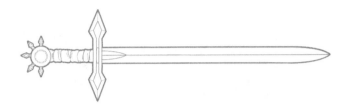

IF YOU WANT TO CONQUER THE WORLD, YOU BEST HAVE DRAGONS.

—George R. R. Martin, *A Dance with Dragons*

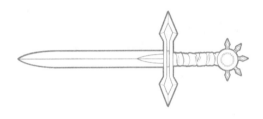

A TRUE HERO ISN'T MEASURED BY
THE SIZE OF HIS STRENGTH, BUT BY
THE STRENGTH OF HIS HEART.

—Disney's *Hercules*

_____
_____
_____
_____
_____
_____
_____
_____

Drogarth

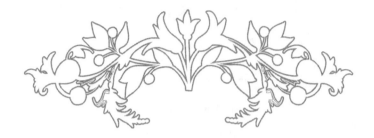

A LIFE WITHOUT ADVENTURE IS LIKELY
TO BE UNSATISFYING.

—Bertrand Russell

_____

_____

_____

_____

_____

_____

_____

_____

_____

_____

Finn the Jackalope Rider

HAVING A LUCK DRAGON WITH YOU IS
THE ONLY WAY TO GO ON A QUEST.

—*The NeverEnding Story*

Tigger the Cat Dragon

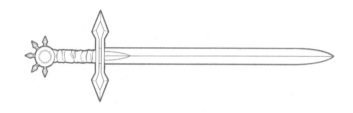

THE LIGHT AT THE END OF THE TUNNEL
MAY BE AN ONCOMING DRAGON.

—Unknown

Ledge Dragon

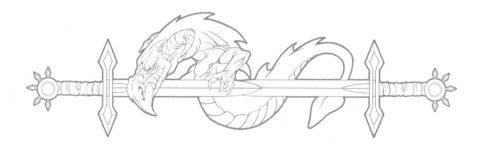

LET US STEP OUT INTO THE
NIGHT AND PURSUE THAT FLIGHTY
TEMPTRESS, ADVENTURE.

—J. K. Rowling, *Harry Potter and the Half-Blood Prince*

Abeytu the Elf

ENEMIES OF THE ORCS ARE LIKELY
TO BE OUR FRIENDS.

—J.R.R. Tolkien, *The Two Towers*

War Orc

FAIRIES HAVE TO BE ONE THING OR THE OTHER,
BECAUSE BEING SO SMALL THEY UNFORTUNATELY
HAVE ROOM FOR ONE FEELING ONLY AT A TIME.

—J. M. Barrie, *Peter Pan*

Flower Fairy

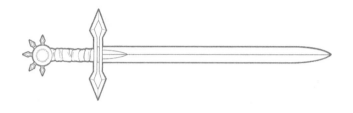

THE DRAGONS COULD NEVER
UNDERSTAND WHY THEY GENERATED
SUCH ABJECT FEAR IN COMMON FOLK.

—Anne McCaffrey, *The Dragonriders of Pern*

Flyn the Eagle-Winged Dragon

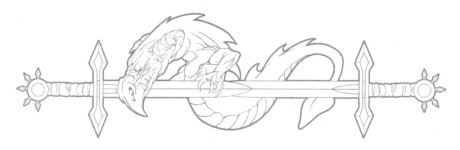

IT IS NOT THE LAND OF MEN. IT IS THE
COUNTRY OF ... FAUNS AND
SATYRS, OF DWARFS AND GIANTS, OF
THE GODS AND THE CENTAURS, OF
TALKING BEASTS.

—C. S. Lewis, *Prince Caspian*

Satyr and the Fairy Trickster

NEVER FEAR QUARRELS, BUT SEEK HAZARDOUS ADVENTURES.

—Alexandre Dumas, *The Three Musketeers*

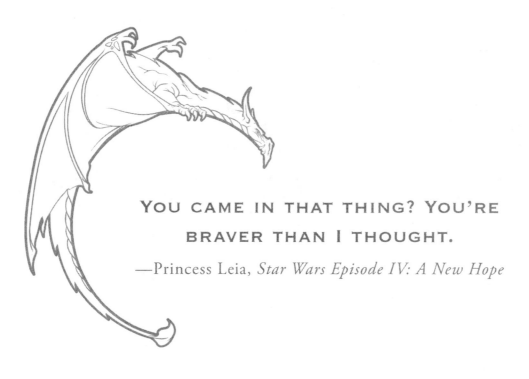

YOU CAME IN THAT THING? YOU'RE
BRAVER THAN I THOUGHT.

—Princess Leia, *Star Wars Episode IV: A New Hope*

_____

_____

_____

_____

_____

_____

_____

_____

Lorale and Friend

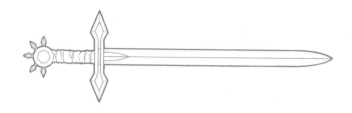

EVERY MAN CAN TRANSFORM
THE WORLD FROM ONE OF MONOTONY
AND DRABNESS TO ONE OF
EXCITEMENT AND ADVENTURE.

—Irving Wallace

THOSE WHO DON'T BELIEVE IN MAGIC
WILL NEVER FIND IT.

—Roald Dahl, *The Minpins*